Favorite Poems

TO READ ALOUD

Illustrated by ART KRUSZ

(Jerry Hammer Associates, Inc.)

Cover design by GYO FUJIKAWA

WONDER BOOKS · NEW YORK

Note to Parents

One of the most gratifying ways of bringing the precious feeling of closeness to your family is sharing the joys of reading with your children. More and more parents are discovering the pleasures of a daily Storytime Hour . . . a time for reading aloud to young children, helping them develop a lifetime love of books, stimulating their imagination, enriching their vocabularies, and teaching them fascinating facts about the world around them.

Read-Aloud books are especially planned for the small child who loves to listen to a story— and also for the beginning reader who is proud of his new talent and wants to show it off for your approval.

You will enjoy reading these stories to your young children. You will enjoy them perhaps even more when your child proudly reads the stories to you.

CONTENTS

LITTLE BOY BLUE

Eugene Field

The little toy dog is covered with dust,
　　But sturdy and staunch he stands;
The little toy soldier is red with rust,
　　And his musket molds in his hands.

Time was when the little toy dog was new,
   And the soldier was passing fair;
And that was the time when our Little Boy
      Blue
   Kissed them and put them there.

"Now, don't you go till I come," he said,
   "And don't you make any noise!"
Then toddling off to his trundle-bed,
   He dreamed of the pretty toys;

And, as he was dreaming, an angel song
   Awakened our Little Boy Blue.
Oh! the years are many, the years are long,
   But the little toy friends are true!

Aye, faithful to Little Boy Blue they stand,
   Each in the same old place,
Awaiting the touch of a little hand,
   The smile on a little face;

And they wonder, as waiting the long years
      through,
   In the dust of that little chair,
What has become of our Little Boy Blue
   Since he kissed them and put them there.

THE LOST DOLL

Charles Kingsley

I once had a dear little doll, dears,
    The prettiest doll in the world;
Her cheeks were so red and so white, dears,
    And her hair was so charmingly curled.
But I lost my poor little doll, dears,
    As I played in the field one day;
And I cried for her more than a week, dears,
    But I never could find where she lay.

I found my poor little doll, dears,
    As I played in the field one day;
Folks say she is terribly changed, dears,
    For her paint is all washed away,
And her arms trodden off by the cows, dears,
    And her hair not the least bit curled;
Yet for old sake's sake, she is still, dears,
    The prettiest doll in the world.

I'M GLAD

I'm glad the sky is painted blue
And the earth is painted green,
With such a lot of nice fresh air
All sandwiched in between.

LITTLE RAINDROPS

Ann Hawkshaw

Where do you come from,
    You little drops of rain;
Pitter-patter, pitter-patter,
    Down the window pane?

They won't let me walk,
    And they won't let me play,
And they won't let me go
    Out of doors all today.

They put away my playthings
    Because I broke them all,
And they locked up all my blocks
    And took away my ball.

8

Tell me, little raindrops,
　　Is that the way you play,
Pitter-patter, pitter-patter,
　　All the rainy day?

They say I'm very naughty,
　　But I've nothing else to do
But sit here at the window;
　　I should like to play with you.

The little raindrops cannot speak,
　　But "pitter-patter-pat"
Means, "We can play on this side.
　　Why can't you play on that?"

WHO HAS SEEN THE WIND?

Christina Rossetti

Who has seen the wind?
　　Neither I nor you:
But when the leaves hang trembling,
　　The wind is passing thro'.

Who has seen the wind?
　　Neither you nor I:
But when the trees bow down their heads,
　　The wind is passing by.

GOOD NIGHT AND GOOD MORNING
Lord Houghton

A fair little girl sat under a tree,
Sewing as long as her eyes could see;
Then she smoothed her work and folded it
    right,
And said to her work, "Good night, good
    night!"

Such a number of rooks flew over her head,
Crying "Caw, caw!" on their way to bed;
And she said as she watched their curious
    flight,
"You little black birds, good night, good
    night!

The horses neighed and the oxen lowed;
And the sheep's "Bleat, bleat!" came over
    the road,
All seeming to say, with quiet delight,
"Good little girl, good night, good night!"

She did not say to the sun, "Good night!"
Though she saw him there like a ball of light;
For she knew he had God's own time to keep
All over the world, and never could sleep.

The tall pink foxglove bowed his head,
The violets curtsied and went to bed;
And good little Lucy tied up her hair,
And said on her knees her favorite prayer.

And while on her pillow she softly lay,
She knew no more till again it was day,
And all things said to the beautiful sun,
"Good morning, good morning, our work has
      begun!"

AROUND THE WORLD
Kate Greenaway

In a go-cart so tiny
    My sister I drew;
And I've promised to draw her
    The wide world through.

We have not yet started—
    I own it with sorrow—
Because our trip's always
    Put off till tomorrow.

THE MONTHS

Sara Coleridge

January brings the snow,
Makes our feet and fingers glow.

February brings the rain,
Thaws the frozen lake again.

March brings breezes loud and shrill,
Stirs the dancing daffodil.

April brings the primrose sweet,
Scatters daisies at our feet.

May brings flocks of pretty lambs,
Skipping by their fleecy dams.

June brings tulips, lilies, roses,
Fills the children's hands with posies.

Hot July brings cooling showers,
Apricots and gillyflowers.

August brings the sheaves of corn;
Then the harvest home is borne.

Warm September brings the fruit;
Sportsmen then begin to shoot.

Fresh October brings the pheasant;
Then to gather nuts is pleasant.

Dull November brings the blast,
When the leaves are whirling fast.

Chill December brings the sleet,
Blazing fires and Christmas treat.

THE MOON
Eliza Lee Follen

Oh, look at the moon!
    She is shining up there;
Oh, Mother, she looks
    Like a lamp in the air.

Last week she was smaller,
    And shaped like a bow;
But now she's grown bigger
    And round as an O.

Pretty moon, pretty moon,
    How you shine on the door,
And make it all bright
    On my nursery floor!

You shine on my playthings,
    And show me their place,
And I love to look up
    At your pretty bright face.

And there is a star
    Close by you, and maybe
That small twinkling star
    Is your little baby.

THE STAR
Jane Taylor

Twinkle, twinkle, little star,
How I wonder what you are!
Up above the world so high,
Like a diamond in the sky.

When the blazing sun is gone,
When he nothing shines upon,
Then you show your little light,
Twinkle, twinkle, all the night.

Then the traveler in the dark
Thanks you for your tiny spark;
He could not tell which way to go
If you did not twinkle so.

In the dark blue sky you keep,
And often through my curtains peep;
For you never shut your eye
Till the sun is in the sky.

As your bright and tiny spark
Lights the traveler in the dark,
Though I know not what you are,
Twinkle, twinkle, little star.

A LITTLE BOY'S POCKET

Do you know what's in my pottet?
Such a lot of treasures in it!
Listen now while I bedin it:
Such a lot of sings it holds,
And everysing dat's in my pottet,
And when and where and how I dot it.
First of all, here's in my pottet
A beauty shell, I pit'd it up:
And here's the handle of a tup
That somebody has broked at tea;
The shell's a hole in it, you see:
Nobody knows dat I dot it,
I teep it safe in my pottet.
And here's my ball, too, in my pottet,
And here's my pennies, one, two, free,

That Aunt Mary dave to me.
Tomorrow I will buy a spade,
When I'm out walking with the maid;
I tan't put dat here in my pottet!
But I can use it when I've dot it.
Here's some more sings in my pottet,
Here's my lead and here's my string;
And once I had an iron ring,
But through a hole it lost one day,
And this is what I always say—
A hole's the worst thing in a pottet,
Be sure and mend it when you've dot it.

BOATS SAIL ON THE RIVERS
Christina Rossetti

Boats sail on the rivers,
    'And ships sail on the seas;
But clouds that sail across the sky
    Are prettier far than these.

There are bridges on the rivers,
    As pretty as you please;
    But the bow that bridges heaven,
    And overtops the trees,
And builds a road from earth to sky,
    Is prettier far than these.

LONG, LONG AGO

Elizabeth Prentiss

Once there was a little kitty,
Whiter than snow;
In a barn she used to frolic,
Long, long ago.

In the barn a little mousie
Ran to and fro;
And she spied the little kitty,
Long, long ago.

Four paws had little kitty,
Paws soft as dough;
And they caught the little mousie,
Long, long ago.

Nine teeth had little kitty,
All in a row;
And they bit the little mousie,
Long, long ago.

When the teeth bit little mousie,
Mousie cried, "Oh!"
But she got away from kitty,
Long, long ago.

WHAT DOES LITTLE BIRDIE SAY?

Alfred Tennyson

What does little birdie say,
In her nest at peep of day?
"Let me fly," says little birdie,
 "Mother, let me fly away."
"Birdie, rest a little longer,
Till the little wings are stronger."
So she rests a little longer,
 Then she flies away.

What does little baby say,
In her bed at peep of day?
Baby says, like little birdie,
 "Let me rise and fly away."
"Baby, sleep a little longer,
Till the little limbs are stronger."
If she sleeps a little longer,
 Baby, too, shall fly away.

THANKSGIVING

Heavenly Father, hear our thanks
 For Thy loving care;
Help us now to show our love,
 And each blessing share.

LITTLE POLLY FLINDERS

Little Polly Flinders
    Sat among the cinders,
Warming her pretty little toes.
     Her mother came and caught her
And spanked her little daughter
    For soiling her nice, new clothes.

THE NORTH WIND DOTH BLOW

The north wind doth blow,
And we shall have snow,
And what will poor robin do then?
    Poor thing!
He'll sit in a barn,
And to keep himself warm,
Will hide his head under his wing.
    Poor thing!

RAINDROPS

Softly the rain goes pitter-patter,
Softly the rain comes falling down.
Hark to the people who hurry by;
Raindrops are footsteps from out the sky!
Softly the rain goes pitter-patter,
Softly the rain comes falling down.

MY KITTY

Constance Willis Camp

I have a darling kitty,
I like to hear her mew,
For that's the way she tells me:
I love you.
Mew, mew, mew,
I love you.

I'll never hurt my kitty,
For if she couldn't mew,
I don't know how she'd tell me:
I love you.
Mew, mew, mew,
I love you.

BLOW, WIND, BLOW!

Blow, wind, blow! and go, mill, go!
That the miller may grind his corn;
That the baker may take it,
And into rolls make it,
And send us some hot in the morn.

BROTHER JOHN

Are you sleeping,
Are you sleeping,
Brother John?
Brother John?
Morning bells are ringing,
Morning bells are ringing,
Ding, ding, dong!
Ding, ding, dong!

BIRD, OH, BIRD, COME UNDER MY BONNET

Bird, oh, bird, come under my bonnet,
And you shall have bread with honey upon it;
You shall have sugar in coffee and tea,
And play every day with baby and me.

QUITE WELL, QUITE WARY

A little girl, quite well and hearty,
Thought she'd like to give a party.
But as her friends were shy and wary,
Nobody came but her own canary.

THERE WAS A LITTLE GIRL

There was a little girl who had a little curl
    Right in the middle of her forehead,
And when she was good, she was very, very
      good,
    But when she was bad, she was horrid.

She stood on her head in her trundle bed,
    With nobody by to hinder;
She screamed and she squalled, she yelled
      and she bawled,
    And drummed her heels on the winder.

Her mother heard the noise, and thought it
      was the boys,
    Playing in the empty attic.
She rushed upstairs and caught her una-
      wares,
    And spanked her most emphatic.

THE DEACON'S MASTERPIECE

Oliver Wendell Holmes

Have you heard of the wonderful one-hoss
    shay,
That was built in such a logical way
It ran a hundred years to a day,
And then, of a sudden, it—ah, but stay,
I'll tell you what happened without delay,
Scaring the parson into fits,
Frightening people out of their wits—
Have you ever heard of that, I say?

Seventeen hundred and fifty-five.
Georgius Secundus was then alive—
Snuffy old drone from the German hive.
That was the year when Lisbon-town
Saw the earth open and gulp her down,
And Braddock's army was done so brown,
It was on the terrible Earthquake-day
That the Deacon finished the one-hoss shay.

Now in building of chaises, I tell you what,
There is always *somewhere* a weakest spot,
In hub, tire, felloe, in spring or thill,
In panel, or crossbar, or floor, or sill,
In screw, bolt, thoroughbrace—lurking still,
Find it somewhere you must and will—
Above or below, or within or without—
And that's the reason, beyond a doubt,
That a chaise *breaks down*, but doesn't *wear
    out*.

But the Deacon swore (as Deacons do,
With an "I dew vum," or an "I tell *yeou*,")
He would build one shay to beat the taown
'N' the keounty 'n' all the kentry raoun';
It should be so built that it *couldn't* break
    daown:

—"Fur," said the Deacon, " 't's mighty plain
Thut the weakes' place mus' stan' the strain;
'N' the way t' fix it, uz I maintain, is only jest
T' make that place uz strong uz the rest.

So the Deacon inquired of the village folk
Where he could find the strongest oak,
That couldn't be split nor bent nor broke,
That was for spokes and floor and sills;
He sent for lancewood to make the thills;
The crossbars were ash, from the straightest
    trees,
The panels of white wood, that cuts like
    cheese,
But lasts like iron for things like these;

The hubs of logs from the "Settler's ellum,"
Last of its timber—they couldn't sell 'em,
Never an axe had seen their chips,
And the wedges flew from between their lips,
Their blunt ends frizzled like celery-tips;
Step and prop-iron, bolt and screw,
Spring, tire, axle, and linchpin too,
Steel of the finest, bright and blue;
Thoroughbrace bison-skin, thick and wide;
Boot, top, dasher, from tough old hide
Found in the pit when the tanner died,

That was the way he "put her through."
"There!" said the Deacon, "naow she'll
  dew!"
Do! I tell you, I rather guess
She was a wonder, and nothing less!
Colts grew horses, beards turned gray,
Deacon and deaconess dropped away,
Children and grandchildren—where were
  they?
But there stood the stout old one-hoss shay
As fresh as on Lisbon-earthquake day!

EIGHTEEN HUNDRED—it came and
  found
The Deacon's masterpiece strong and sound.
Eighteen hundred increased by ten—
"Hahnsum kerridge" they called it then.
Eighteen hundred and twenty came—
Running as usual; much the same;
Thirty and forty at last arrive,
And then came fifty, and FIFTY-FIVE.

Little of all we value here
Wakes on the morn of its hundredth year
Without both feeling and looking queer.
In fact, there's nothing that keeps its youth,
So far as I know, but a tree and truth.

(This is a moral that runs at large;
Take it—You're welcome—No extra
   charge.)

FIRST OF NOVEMBER—the Earthquake-
   day—
There are traces of age in the one-hoss shay,
A general flavor of mild decay,
But nothing local, as one may say.
There couldn't be—for the Deacon's art
Had made it so like in every part
That there wasn't a chance for one to start.
For the wheels were just as strong as the
   thills,
And the floor was just as strong as the sills,
And the panels just as strong as the floor,
And the whipple-tree neither less nor more,
And the back-crossbar as strong as the fore,

And spring and axle and hub encore.
And yet, *as a whole*, it is past a doubt
In another hour it will be *worn out!*

Now, small boys, get out of the way!
FIRST OF NOVEMBER, 'Fifty-five!
This morning the parson takes a drive.
Here comes the wonderful one-hoss shay,
Drawn by a rat-tailed, ewe-necked bay.
"Huddup!" said the parson. Off went they.
The parson was working on his Sunday's
    text,
Had got to *fifthly*, and stopped perplexed
At what the—Moses—was coming next.
All at once the horse stood still,
Close by the meet'n'-house on the hill.
First a shiver, and then a thrill,
Then something decidedly like a spill—
And the parson was sitting upon a rock,
At half-past nine by the meet'n'-house
    clock—
Just the hour of the Earthquake shock!

What do you think the parson found,
When he got up and stared around?
The poor old chaise in a heap or mound,
As if it had been to the mill and ground!

You see, of course, if you're not a dunce,
How it went to pieces all at once,
All at once, and nothing first—
Just as bubbles do when they burst.

End of the wonderful one-hoss shay.
Logic is logic. That's all I say.

AN OPEN SECRET

Pussy Willow had a secret
 That the snowdrops whispered her,
And she purred it to the south wind,
 While it stroked her velvet fur;
And the south wind hummed it softly
 To the busy honey bees,
And they buzzed it to the blossoms
 On the scarlet maple trees.

And these dropped it to the wood brooks
 Brimming full of melted snow,
And the brooks told Robin Redbreast
 As he chattered to and fro;
Little Robin could not keep it,
 So he sang it loud and clear
To the sleepy hills and meadows,
 "Wake up! Cheer up! Spring is here!"

SWEET AND LOW

Alfred Tennyson

Sweet and low, sweet and low,
   Wind of the western sea!
Low, low, breathe and blow,
   Wind of the western sea!
Over the rolling waters go,
Come from the dying moon, and blow,
   Blow him again to me;
While my little one, while my pretty one
     sleeps.

Sleep and rest, sleep and rest,
   Father will come to thee soon;
Rest, rest, on Mother's breast,
   Father will come to thee soon;
Father will come to his babe in the nest,
Silver sails all out of the west
   Under the silver moon:
Sleep, my little one, sleep, my pretty one,
     sleep.

FIVE LITTLE CHICKENS

Said the first little chicken,
With a queer little squirm,
"Oh, I wish I could find
A fat little worm!"

Said the second little chicken,
With an odd little shrug,
"Oh, I wish I could find
A fat little bug!"

Said the third little chicken,
With a little sigh of grief,
"Oh, I wish I could find
A little green leaf!"

Said the fourth little chicken,
With a sharp little squeal,
"Oh, I wish I could find
Some nice yellow meal!"

Said the fifth little chicken,
With a faint little moan,
"I wish I could find
A wee gravel stone!"

"Now, see here," said their mother
From the green garden patch,
"If you want any breakfast,
You must all come and scratch!"

RAIN, RAIN, GO AWAY

Rain, rain, go away,
Come again some other day.

Rain, rain, go to Spain,
Never show your face again.

TAKING OFF

Mary McB. Green

The airplane taxis down the field
And heads into the breeze;
It lifts its wheels above the ground,
It skims above the trees;
It rises high and higher,
Away up toward the sun;
It's just a speck against the sky—
And now it's gone!

THE OWL AND THE PUSSYCAT

Edward Lear

The Owl and the Pussycat went to sea
    In a beautiful pea-green boat;
They took some honey, and plenty of money
    Wrapped up in a five-pound note.
The Owl looked up to the stars above,
    And sang to a small guitar,
"O lovely Pussy, O Pussy, my love,
    What a beautiful Pussy you are,
      You are,
      You are!
    What a beautiful Pussy you are!"

Pussy said to the Owl, "You elegant fowl,
        How charmingly sweet you sing!
Oh! let us be married; too long we have tar-
        ried:
        But what shall we do for a ring?"
They sailed away, for a year and a day,
        To the land where the bong-tree grows,
And there in a wood a Piggy-wig stood,
        With a ring at the end of his nose,
            His nose,
            His nose,
        With a ring at the end of his nose.

"Dear Pig, are you willing to sell for one
        shilling
        Your ring?" Said the Piggy, "I will."
So they took it away, and were married next
        day
        By the turkey who lives on the hill.
They dined on mince and slices of quince,
        Which they ate with a runcible spoon;
And hand in hand, on the edge of the sand,
        They danced by the light of the moon,
            The moon,
            The moon,
        They danced by the light of the moon.

A TRAGIC STORY

Albert Von Chamisso
Translated by William M. Thackeray

There lived a sage in days of yore,
And he a handsome pigtail wore;
But wondered much, and sorrowed more,
Because it hung behind him.

He mused upon this curious case,
And swore he'd change the pigtail's place,
And have it hanging at his face,
Not dangling there behind him.

Says he, "The mystery I've found,
I'll turn me round,"—he turned him round,
But still it hung behind him.

Then round and round, and out and in,
All day the puzzled sage did spin;
In vain—it mattered not a pin—
The pigtail hung behind him.

And right and left, and roundabout,
And up and down and in and out
He turned; but still the pigtail stout
Hung steadily behind him.

And though his efforts never slack,
And though he twist, and twirl, and tack,
Alas! still faithful to his back,
The pigtail hangs behind him.

THE COCK DOTH CROW

The cock doth crow
To let you know
If you be wise,
'Tis time to rise.

A FARMER WENT TROTTING

A farmer went trotting upon his gray mare,
    Bumpety, bumpety, bump!
With his daughter behind him, so rosy and
    fair,
    Bumpety, bumpety, bump!
A raven cried, "Croak!" and they all tumbled
    down,
    Lumpety, lumpety, lump!
The mare broke her knees, and the farmer
    his crown,
    Lumpety, lumpety, lump!
The mischievous raven flew laughing away,
    Bumpety, bumpety, bump!
And vowed he would serve them the same the
    next day,
    Lumpety, lumpety, lump!

RUNAWAY BROOK

Eliza Lee Follen

"Stop, stop, pretty water!"
    Said Mary one day,
To a frolicsome brook
    That was running away.

"You run on so fast:
     I wish you would stay;
My boat and my flowers
     You will carry away.

"But I will run after;
     Mother says that I may,
For I would know where
     You are running away."

So Mary ran on;
     But I have heard say,
That she never could find
     Where the brook ran away

SYSTEM

Robert Louis Stevenson

Every night my prayers I say
And get my dinner every day;
And every day that I've been good,
I get an orange after food.

The child that is not clean and neat,
With lots of toys and things to eat,
He is a naughty child, I'm sure,
Or else his dear papa is poor.

THE MILLER HE GRINDS

The miller he grinds his corn, his corn;
The miller he grinds his corn, his corn;
The little boy blue comes winding his horn,
With a hop, step, and a jump.

The carter he whistles aside his team;
The carter he whistles aside his team;
And Dolly come tripping with nice thick
    cream,
With a hop, step, and a jump.

The nightingale sings when we're at rest;
The nightingale sings when we're at rest;
The little bird climbs the tree for his rest,
With a hop, step, and a jump.

The damsels are churning for curds and
    whey;
The damsels are churning for curds and
    whey;
The lads in the field are making the hay,
With a hop, step, and a jump.

WHERE ARE YOU GOING, MY PRETTY MAID?

"Where are you going, my pretty maid?"
"I'm going a-milking, sir," she said.
"May I go with you, my pretty maid?"
"You're kindly welcome, sir," she said.

"What is your father, my pretty maid?"
"My father's a farmer, sir," she said.
"What is your fortune, my pretty maid?"
"My face is my fortune, sir," she said.

"Then I can't marry you, my pretty maid!"
"Nobody asked you, sir!" she said.

LITTLE ROBIN

Pit, pat, well-a-day!
Little Robin flew away;
Where can little Robin be?
Gone into the cherry tree.

LITTLE GIRL, LITTLE GIRL

Little girl, little girl, where have you been?
Gathering roses to give to the Queen.
Little girl, little girl, what gave she you?
She gave me a diamond as big as my shoe.

SAILING

I see a ship a-sailing, sailing, sailing,
I see a ship a-sailing, sailing out to sea;
The captain at the railing, railing, railing,
The captain at the railing waves his hand to
    me.

I see a ship a-rolling, rolling, rolling,
I see a ship a-rolling, rolling home from sea;
I hear its bell a-tolling, tolling, tolling,
I hear its bell a-tolling, coming back to me.

I'LL SING YOU A SONG

I'll sing you a song—
Though not very long,
Yet I think it as pretty as any;
Put your hand in your purse,
You'll never be worse,
And give the poor singer a penny.

CRADLE SONG

Isaac Watts

Hush, my babe, lie still and slumber,
Holy angels guard thy bed;
Heav'nly blessings without number,
Gently falling on thy head.

DID YOU EVER SEE A LASSIE?

Did you ever see a lassie, a lassie, a lassie,
Did you ever see a lassie do this way and
that?
Do this way and that way,
Do this way and that way,
Did you ever see a lassie do this way and
that?

THE FAIRIES

William Allingham

Up the airy mountain,
        Down the rushy glen,
We daren't go a-hunting,
        For fear of little men.
Wee folk, good folk,
        Trooping all together;
Green jacket, red cap,
        And white owl's feather!

Down along the rocky shore
  Some make their home.
They live on crispy pancakes
  Of yellow tide-foam;
Some in the reeds
  Of the black mountain-lake,
With frogs for their watch-dogs,
  All night awake.

High on the hilltop
  The old King sits;
He is now so old and gray,
  He's nigh lost his wits.
With a bridge of white mist
  Columbkill he crosses,
On his stately journeys
  From Slieveleague to Rosses;
Or going up with music
  On cold starry nights,
To sup with the Queen
  Of the gay Northern Lights.

They stole little Bridget
  For seven years long;
When she came down again,
  Her friends were all gone.

They took her lightly back,
 Between the night and morrow;
They thought that she was fast asleep,
 But she was dead with sorrow.
They have kept her ever since
 Deep within the lake,
On a bed of flag-leaves,
 Watching till she wake.

By the craggy hillside,
 Through the mosses bare,
They have planted thorn trees
 For pleasure here and there.
Is any man so daring
 As dig them up in spite,
He shall find their sharpest thorns
 In his bed at night.

Up the airy mountain,
 Down the rushy glen,
We daren't go a-hunting
 For fear of little men.
Wee folk, good folk,
 Trooping all together;
Green jacket, red cap,
 And white owl's feather!

BIRD THOUGHTS

Charlotte Brewster Jordan

I lived first in a little house,
 And lived there very well;
I thought the world was small and round,
 And made of pale blue shell.

I lived next in a little nest,
 Nor needed any other;
I thought the world was made of straw,
 And brooded by my mother.

One day I fluttered from the nest
 To see what I could find.
I said, "The world is made of leaves;
 I have been very blind."

At length I flew beyond the tree,
 Quite fit for grown-up labors.
I don't know how the world *is* made,
 And neither do my neighbors!

MY KINGDOM

Louisa M. Alcott

A little kingdom I possess
    Where thoughts and feelings dwell,
And very hard I find the task
    Of governing it well;
For passion tempts and troubles me,
    A wayward will misleads,
And selfishness its shadow casts
    On all my words and deeds.

How can I learn to rule myself,
  To be the child I should,
Honest and brave, nor ever tire
  Of trying to be good?
How can I keep a sunny soul
  To shine along life's way?
How can I tune my little heart
  To sweetly sing all day?

Dear Father, help me with the love
  That casteth out my fear,
Teach me to lean on thee, and feel
  That thou art very near,
That no temptation is unseen,
  No childish grief too small,
Since Thou, with patience infinite,
  Doth soothe and comfort all.

I do not ask for any crown
  But that which all may win,
Nor seek to conquer any world,
  Except the one within.
Be Thou my guide until I find,
  Led by a tender hand,
Thy happy kingdom in *myself*,
  And dare to take command.

WAITING FOR SOMETHING TO TURN UP

Alice Cary

"And why do you throw down your hoe by
    the way
    As if that furrow were done?"
It was the good farmer, Bartholomew Grey
    That spoke on this wise to his son.

Now Barty the younger was not very bad,
    But he didn't take kindly to work,
And the father had oftentimes said of the lad
    That the thing he did best was to shirk!

It was early in May, and a beautiful morn—
    The rosebuds tipped softly with red—
The pea putting on her white bloom, and the
    corn
    Being just gotten up out of bed.

And after the first little break of the day
   Had broadened itself on the blue,
The provident farmer, Bartholomew Grey,
   Had driven afield through the dew.

His brown mare, Fair Fanny, in collar and
     harness
   Went before him, so sturdy and stout,
And ere the sun's fire yet had kindled to
     flames,
   They had furrowed the field twice about.

And still as they came to the southerly
     slope
   He reined in Fair Fanny with "Whoa!"
And gazed toward the homestead, and gazed
     in the hope
   Of seeing young Barty—but no!

"Asleep yet?" he said. "In a minute the
     horn
   That shall call to the breakfast, will
     sound,
And all these long rows of the tender young
     corn
   Left choking and plowed in the ground!"

Now this was the work which the farmer had
       planned
    For Barty—a task kindly meant
To follow the plow, with the hoe in his
      hand,
    And to set up the stalks as he went.

But not till the minutes to hours had run,
    And the heat was aglow far and wide,
Did he see his slow-footed and sleepy-eyed
      son
    A-dragging his hoe by his side.

Midway of the cornfield he stopped, gaped
      around.
    "What use is there working?" says he,
And saying so, threw himself flat on the
      ground
    In the shade of a wide-spreading tree.

And this was the time that Bartholomew
      Grey,
    Fearing bad things might come to the
      worst,
Drew rein on Fair Fanny, the sweat wiped
      away,
    And spoke as we quoted at first.

He had thought to have given the lad such a
    start
    As would bring him at once to his feet,
And he stood in the furrow, amazed, as
    young Bart,
    Lying lazy, and smiling so sweet,

Replied, "The world owes me a living, you
    see,
    And something, or sooner or late,
I'm certain as can be, will turn up for me,
    And I am contented to wait!"

"My son," says the farmer, "take this to your
    heart,
    For to live in the world is to learn,
The good things that *turn up* are for the
    most part
    The things we ourselves help to turn!

"So, boy, if you want to be sure of your bread
    Ere the good time of working is gone,
Brush the cobwebs of nonsense all out of
    your head
    And take up your hoe, and move on!"

THE TABLE AND THE CHAIR

Edward Lear

Said the Table to the Chair,
"You can hardly be aware
How I suffer from the heat
And from chilblains on my feet.
If we took a little walk,
We might have a little talk;
Pray let us take the air,"
Said the Table to the Chair.

Said the Chair unto the Table,
"Now, you *know* we are not able.
How foolishly you talk,
When you know we *cannot* walk!"
Said the Table with a sigh,
"It can do no harm to try.
I've as many legs as you.
Why can't we walk on two?"

So they both went slowly down,
And walked about the town
With a cheerful bumpy sound
As they toddled round and round;
And everybody cried,
As they hastened to their side,
"See! The Table and the Chair
Have come out to take the air!"

But in going down an alley
To a castle in a valley,
They completely lost their way,
And wandered all the day;
Till, to see them safely back,
They paid a Ducky-quack,
And a Beetle, and a Mouse,
Who took them to their house.

Then they whispered to each other
"Oh, delightful little brother,
What a lovely walk we've taken!
Let us dine on beans and bacon."
So the Ducky and the leetle
Browny-Mousy and the Beetle
Dined and danced upon their heads
Till they toddled to their beds.

HOW CREATURES MOVE

The lion walks on padded paws,
The squirrel leaps from limb to limb,
While flies can crawl straight up a wall,
And seals can dive and swim.
The worm, he wiggles all around,
The monkey swings by his tail,
And birds may hop upon the ground,
Or spread their wings and sail.
But boys and girls have much more fun;
They leap and dance
And walk and run.

WHITE BUTTERFLIES
Algernon Charles Swinburne

Fly, white butterflies, out to sea,
Frail, pale wings for the wind to try,
Small white wings that we scarce can see,
      Fly!

Some fly light as a laugh of glee,
Some fly soft as a long, low sigh;
All to the haven where each would be,
      Fly!

DAFFODILS

William Wordsworth

I wandered lonely as a cloud
That floats on high o'er vales and hills,
When all at once I saw a crowd—
A host of golden daffodils
Beside the lake, beneath the trees,
Fluttering and dancing in the breeze.

Continuous as the stars that shine
And twinkle on the Milky Way,
They stretched in never-ending line
Along the margin of a bay:
Ten thousand saw I, at a glance,
Tossing their heads in sprightly dance.

CATKIN

I have a little pussy,
    And her coat is silver gray;
She lives in a great wide meadow
    And she never runs away.
She always is a pussy,
    She'll never be a cat
Because—she's a pussy willow!
    Now what do you think of that.

GENERAL WASHINGTON

When General Washington was young,
    About as big as I,
He never would permit his tongue
    To tell a willful lie.

Once when he cut his father's tree,
    He owned it to his face;
And then his father ardently
    Clasped him in his embrace.

He told his son it pleased him more
    To find him own the truth,
Than if his tree were bending o'er
    With rich and golden fruit.

Then, like this good and noble youth,
    Whose virtues ever shone,
I'll seek the paths of love and truth,
    And all my faults will own.

THREE LITTLE TREES

A dear little secret,
As sweet as could be,
The breeze told one day
To the glad apple tree.
The breeze told the apple,
The apple the plum,
The plum told the pear,
"Robin Redbreast has come."

THE GOLDEN RULE

To do to others as I would
    That they should do to me,
Will make me gentle, kind and good,
    As children ought to be.

MELONS

Mary Mapes Dodge

Melons! Melons!
   All day long
Joe's mother sits
   Selling melons.
"Ho! Ripe and rich!"
   Is her song,
All day long
   Selling melons.

Melons! Melons!
   All day long
Joe walks the street
   Selling melons.
"Ho! Ripe and sweet!"
   Is his song,
All day long
   Selling melons.

THE ALPHABET

A, B, C, D, E, F, G,
H, I, J, K, L, M, N, O, P,
Q, R, S, T, U and V,
W, X and Y and Z.

STATELY VERSE

If Mary goes far out to sea,
  By wayward breezes fanned,
I'd like to know—can you tell me?—
  Just where would Maryland?

If Tenny went high up in air
  And looked o'er land and sea,
Look here and there and everywhere,
  Pray what would Tennessee?

I looked out of the window and
  Saw Orry on the lawn;
He's not there now, and who can tell
  Just where has Oregon?

Two girls were quarreling one day
  With garden tools, and so
I said, "My dears, let Mary rake
  And just let Idaho."

An English lady had a steed.
  She called him 'Ighland Bay.
She rode for exercise, and thus
  Rhode Island every day.

THE SWING

Robert Louis Stevenson

How do you like to go up in a swing,
Up in the air so blue?
Oh, I do think it the pleasantest thing
Ever a child can do!

Up in the air and over the wall,
Till I can see so wide,
Rivers and trees and cattle and all
Over the countryside—

Till I look down on the garden green,
Down on the roof so brown—
Up in the air I go flying again,
Up in the air and down!

WHEN MOTHER READS ALOUD

When Mother reads aloud, the past
    Seems real as every day;
I hear the tramp of armies vast,
I see the spears and lances cast,
    I join the thrilling fray;
Brave knights and ladies fair and proud
I meet when Mother reads aloud.

When Mother reads aloud, far lands
    Seem very near and true;
I cross the desert's gleaming sands,
Or hunt the jungle's prowling bands,
    Or sail the ocean blue.
Far heights, whose peaks the cold mist
        shroud,
I scale, when Mother reads aloud.

When Mother reads aloud, I long
    For noble deeds to do—
To help the right, redress the wrong;
It seems so easy to be strong,
    So simple to be true.
Oh, thick and fast the visions crowd
My eyes, when Mother reads aloud.

THE KAYAK

Over the briny wave I go,
In spite of the weather, in spite of the snow:
What cares the hardy Eskimo?
In my little skiff, with paddle and lance,
I glide where the foaming billows dance.

Round me the sea-birds slip and soar;
Like me, they love the ocean's roar.
Sometimes a floating iceberg gleams
Above me with its melting streams;
Sometimes a rushing wave will fall
Down on my skiff and cover it all.

But what care I for a wave's attack?
With my paddle I right my little kayak,
And then its weight I speedily trim,
And over the water away I skim.

IN THE MEADOW

Christina Rossetti

In the meadow—what is in the meadow?
Bluebells, buttercups, meadowsweet,
And fairy rings for children's feet,
In the meadow.

THE FIRST SNOWFALL

James Russell Lowell

The snow had begun in the gloaming,
 And busily all the night
Had been heaping field and highway
 With a silence deep and white.

Every pine and fir and hemlock
 Wore ermine too dear for an earl,
And the poorest twig on the elm tree
 Was ridged inch deep with pearl.

THE SHOEMAKER

As I was a-walking the other day,
I peeped in a window just over the way
And old and bent and feeble, too,
There sat an old cobbler a-making a shoe.
With a rack-a-tac-tac and a rack-a-tac-too,
This is the way he makes a shoe.
With a bright little awl he makes a hole,
Right through the upper, and then through
 the sole,
He puts in a peg, he puts in two,
And then with a smile he hammers it
 through.

THE GINGERBREAD MAN

A little old lady
Once took a flat pan
And made for her husband
A Gingerbread Man.

The strange little man was made in this wise,
He had almonds for fingers, and currants for
     eyes;
He was dressed in the brownest of brown
     little suits,
With little brown trousers and tiny brown
     boots.

As the man to her husband the old lady bore,
He suddenly jumped from the pan to the
floor,
And scampered as fast as his little brown
feet
Would carry him, into the quaint little street.

The old lady's husband,
Who wanted a bite,
Ran out to prevent
Mr. Gingerbread's flight.

The good wife came after,
But quicker than she
Was a brisk little dog
Who was out for a spree.

The little brown man cared never a pin;
He ran past the dog, crying out with a grin
(While Doggie barked loudly and on they all
    ran),
"You cannot catch me, I'm the Gingerbread
    Man!"

The little old lady ran well in the hunt,
And so did her husband, with Doggie in
    front;
But the Gingerbread Man laughed aloud in
    his glee,
"Though you all may be clever, you cannot
    catch me!"

A big tabby cat
With a very fierce face
Saw Gingerbread coming
And took up the chase.

A sturdy policeman,
Slow-pacing his beat,
Fell in with the others
And raced down the street.

The little brown man ran quicker and
    quicker.

The crowd at his heels grew thicker and
    thicker.
All shouted as loud as they could while they
    ran,
"Stop, thief! He's a runaway Gingerbread
    Man!"

They chased him for many and many a mile,
But Gingerbread Man ran in wonderful
    style.
Sighed the policeman, "I wonder if ever we
    can
Catch up with this fleet-footed Gingerbread
    Man."

A dapper young soldier
Next took up the chase,
Though nothing he knew
Of the facts of the case.

Then a horse, with a neigh,
Bounded into the throng,
And with clattering hoofs
Galloped madly along.

Uphill and downhill the race did not pause,
For all were determined to stick to the cause;

With ease did the Gingerbread Man keep
    ahead,
But many behind him were very near dead.

They dashed into valleys; they raced over
    hills;
They splashed into cool little silvery rills;
They climbed over gates, and they leaped
    over stiles;
They ran and they shouted for hundreds of
    miles.

A gentle old cow,
By the noise frantic sent,
Rushed into the crowd,
Raising dust as she went.

And a clever old crow
Left his favorite tree
To follow the chase
With the greatest of glee.

On through the country, and on through the
    towns;
On through the forests, and over the downs;
And when he looked back at the hurrying
    crowd,

The little brown man felt exceedingly proud!

The dog and the cat, the horse and the cow,
The crow and the soldier, were all panting
    now;
The little old lady was weary indeed,
Although she kept on at a marvelous speed.

A sleepy-eyed owl
Woke and stared at the sight.
Then, spreading his wings,
Joined the crow in the flight.

Some threshers at work
In a barnyard with flails
Took quick to their heels
And leaped over the rails.

But though the crowd grew, and increased as
    time went,
The little brown man seemed extremely con-
    tent,
And laughed as he saw how they all ran and
    ran,
And yet couldn't catch him—the Ginger-
    bread Man.

He capered in frolic, he shouted with glee:
"For all you're so many, you cannot catch
    me!
Although you are running as fast as you can,
I'm faster, for I am the Gingerbread Man!"

Some mowers were mowing
A meadow hard by,
But couldn't resist
The hue and the cry.

What shrieking and shouting arose as they
    sped

In chase of the man made of sweet ginger-
    bread!
Some fell on their faces, hard pushed from
    behind,
But picked themselves up, and not one
    seemed to mind.

The threshers, the mowers, the horse, and the
    crow
Were all out of breath, but continued to go,
But the dog and the cat, although hot, did the
    best,
And ran, with their tongues out, in front of
    the rest.

In fact, with such zeal and such vigor they
    ran,
They might have caught up with the Ginger-
    bread Man;
When, all of a sudden, he turned to the right,
Scrambled over a wall, and was lost to their
    sight.

But there was a river
With rushes and rocks,
And high on the bank sat
A wily old fox.

"Oh, where are you going, my Gingerbread
   Man?"
Asked the fox. "I will help you along, if I can.
Although I'm a fox, I can swim like a fish,
And will take you across on my back, if you
   wish."

The little brown man thanked the fox with a
   bow,
And said, "If you're ready, I'll go with you
   now."
He jumped on his muzzle in less than a
   trice . . .
But foxes are cunning and ginger is nice!

And Gingerbread vanished
In less than a twink.
Now where did he go to?
I leave you to think!

STAR WISH

Star light, star bright,
First star I see tonight,
I wish I may, I wish I might
Have the wish I wish tonight.

GRASSHOPPER GREEN

Grasshopper Green is a comical chap;
    He lives on the best of fare.
Bright little trousers, jacket, and cap,
    These are his summer wear.
Out in the meadow he loves to go,
    Playing away in the sun;
It's hopperty, skipperty, high and low,
    Summer's the time for fun.

Grasshopper Green has a quaint little house;
    It's under the hedge so gay.
Grandmother Spider, as still as a mouse,
    Watches him over the way.
Gladly he's calling the children, I know,
    Out in the beautiful sun;
It's hopperty, skipperty, high and low,
    Summer's the time for fun.

HALLOWEEN

Heyhow for Halloween,
When all the witches are to be seen,
Some in black and some in green,
Heyhow for Halloween.

WYNKEN, BLYNKEN, AND NOD

Eugene Field

Wynken, Blynken, and Nod one night
    Sailed off in a wooden shoe—
Sailed on a river of crystal light,
    Into a sea of dew.
"Where are you going, and what do you
       wish?"
    The old moon asked the three.
"We have come to fish for the herring fish
    That live in this beautiful sea;
    Nets of silver and gold have we!"
        Said Wynken,
        Blynken,
        And Nod.

The old moon laughed and sang a song,
        As they rocked in the wooden shoe;
And the wind that sped them all night long
        Ruffled the waves of dew.
The little stars were the herring fish
        That lived in the beautiful sea.
"Now cast your nets wherever you wish—
        Never afeared are we!"
        So cried the stars to the fishermen three,
                Wynken,
                Blynken,
                And Nod.

All night long their nets they threw
        To the stars in the twinkling foam—
Then down from the skies came the wooden
        shoe,
        Bringing the fishermen home:
'Twas all so pretty a sail, it seemed
        As if it could not be;
And some folks thought 'twas a dream they'd
        dreamed
        Of sailing that beautiful sea;
        But I shall name you the fishermen
        three:
                Wynken,
                Blynken,
                And Nod.

Wynken and Blynken are two little eyes,
    And Nod is a little head,
And the wooden shoe that sailed the skies
    Is a wee one's trundle bed;
So shut your eyes while Mother sings
    Of wonderful sights that be,
And you shall see the beautiful things
    As you rock in the misty sea
    Where the old shoe rocked the fishermen
       three:
           Wynken,
           Blynken,
           And Nod.

THE MAN IN THE MOON

The Man in the Moon, as he sails the sky,
Is a very remarkable skipper.
But he made a mistake
When he tried to take
A drink of milk from the Dipper.
He dipped right into the Milky Way
And slowly and carefully filled it.
The Big Bear growled
And the Little Bear howled,
And frightened him so, he spilled it.

CLOUDS

Christina Rossetti

White sheep, white sheep,
On a blue hill,
When the wind stops
You all stand still.
When the wind blows
You walk away slow.
White sheep, white sheep,
Where do you go?

SNOWFLAKES

Mary Mapes Dodge

Whenever a snowflake leaves the sky,
It turns and turns to say, "Good-by!
Good-by, dear cloud, so cool and gray!"
Then lightly travels on its way.

THE WEST WIND

Percy Bysshe Shelley

The trumpet of a prophecy! O Wind,
If winter comes, can spring be far behind?

THE SUGARPLUM TREE

Eugene Field

Have you ever heard of the Sugarplum Tree?
    'Tis a marvel of great renown!
It blooms on the shore of the Lollipop Sea
    In the garden of Shut-eye Town;
The fruit that it bears is so wondrously sweet
    (As those who have tasted it say)
That good little children have only to eat
    Of that fruit to be happy next day.

When you've got to the tree, you would **have**
    a hard time
    To capture the fruit which I sing;
The tree is so tall that no person could **climb**
    To the boughs where the sugarplums
    swing!

But up in that tree sits a chocolate cat,
    And a gingerbread dog prowls below—
And this is the way you contrive to get at
    Those sugarplums tempting you so:

You say but the word to that gingerbread dog
    And he barks with such terrible zest
That the chocolate cat is at once all agog,
    As her swelling proportions attest.
And the chocolate cat goes cavorting around
    From this leafy limb unto that,
And the sugarplums tumble, of course, to the
        ground—
    Hurrah for that chocolate cat!

There are marshmallows, gumdrops, and
        peppermint canes,
    With stripings of scarlet or gold,
And you carry away of the treasure that
        rains
    As much as your apron can hold!
So come, little child, cuddle closer to me
    In your dainty white nightcap and gown,
And I'll rock you away to that Sugarplum
        Tree
    In the garden of Shut-eye Town.

GUIDANCE

Priscilla Pointer

When I fall, I will call
And know that You will hear me.

Where'er I go, I will know
Loving hands are near me.

I will pray every day
That You will ever guide me.

I can smile all the while
With You here beside me.

PIPPA'S SONG

Robert Browning

The year's at the spring,
And day's at the morn;
Morning's at seven;
The hillside's dew-pearled;
The lark's on the wing;
The snail's on the thorn;
God's in His Heaven—
All's right with the world!

PROTECTION

Priscilla Pointer

When I go to bed at night,
I know that God is near.
He will keep me safe and snug
And nothing need I fear.

He will protect me in the dark
And guard me in the day,
And though I fall, I can't be hurt
If I will live His way.

For God will guide me when awake
And watch me while I sleep,
And I will be good for His sake
And His commandments keep.

GOOD NIGHT

Victor Hugo

Good night! Good night!
Far flies the light;
But still God's love
Shall flame above,
Making all bright.
Good night! Good night!

MY SHADOW

Robert Louis Stevenson

I have a little shadow that goes in and out
    with me,
And what can be the use of him is more than
    I can see.
He is very, very like me from the heels up to
    the head;
And I see him jump before me, when I jump
    into my bed.

The funniest thing about him is the way he
    likes to grow—
Not at all like proper children, which is al-
    ways very slow;
For he sometimes shoots up taller like an
    India-rubber ball,
And he sometimes gets so little that there's
    none of him at all.

He hasn't got a notion of how children ought
    to play,
And can only make a fool of me in every sort
    of way.
He stays so close beside me, he's a coward
    you can see;
I'd think shame to stick to nursie as that
    shadow sticks to me!

One morning, very early, before the sun was
    up,
I rose and found the shining dew on every
    buttercup;
But my lazy little shadow, like an arrant
    sleepyhead,
Had stayed at home behind me and was fast
    asleep in bed.

FOUR DUCKS ON A POND

William Allingham

Four ducks on a pond,
A grass-bank beyond,
A blue sky of spring,
White clouds on the wing—
What a little thing
To remember for years!
To remember with tears!

OH, FAIR TO SEE

Christina Rossetti

Oh, fair to see
Bloom-laden cherry tree,
    Arrayed in sunny white:
    An April day's delight,
Oh, fair to see!

Oh, fair to see
Fruit-laden cherry tree,
    With balls of shining red
    Decking a leafy head,
Oh, fair to see!

TREES

Sara Coleridge

The oak is called the king of trees;
The aspen quivers in the breeze;
The poplar grows up straight and tall;
The pear tree spreads along the wall;
The sycamore gives pleasant shade;
The willow droops in watery glade;
The fir tree useful timber gives;
The beech amid the forest lives.

A KITE

Frank Dempster Sherman

I often sit and wish that I
Could be a kite up in the sky,
And ride upon the breeze and go
Whichever way I chanced to blow.
Then I could look beyond the town,
And see the river winding down,
And follow all the ships that sail
Like me before the merry gale,
Until at last with them I came
To some place with a foreign name.

HIAWATHA'S CHILDHOOD

Henry Wadsworth Longfellow

By the shores of Gitchee Gumee,
By the shining Big-Sea-Water,
Stood the wigwam of Nokomis,
Daughter of the Moon, Nokomis.
Dark behind it rose the forest,
Rose the black and gloomy pine trees,
Rose the firs with cones upon them;
Bright before it beat the water,
Beat the clear and sunny water,
Beat the shining Big-Sea-Water.

There the wrinkled old Nokomis
Nursed the little Hiawatha,
Rocked him in his linden cradle,
Bedded soft in moss and rushes,
Safely bound with reindeer sinews;
Stilled his fretful wail by saying,
"Hush! the Naked Bear will hear thee!"
Lulled him into slumber, singing,
"Ewa-yea! my little owlet!
Who is this that lights the wigwam?
With his great eyes light the wigwam?
Ewa-yea! my little owlet!"

Many things Nokomis taught him
Of the stars that shine in heaven;
Showed him Ishkoodah, the comet,
Ishkoodah, with fiery tresses;
Showed the Death-Dance of the spirits,
Warriors with their plumes and war-clubs,
Flaring far away to northward
In the frosty nights of Winter;
Showed the broad white road in heaven,
Pathway of the ghosts, the shadows,
Running straight across the heavens,
Crowded with the ghosts, the shadows.

At the door on summer evenings
Sat the little Hiawatha;
Heard the whispering of the pine trees,
Heard the lapping of the water,
Sounds of music, words of wonder;
"Minne-wawa!" said the pine trees.
"Mudway-aushka!" said the water.

Saw the firefly, Wah-wah-taysee,
Flitting through the dusk of evening,
With the twinkle of its candle
Lighting up the brakes and bushes,
And he sang the song of children,
Sang the song Nokomis taught him:
"Wah-wah-taysee, little firefly,
Little, flitting, white-fire insect,
Little, dancing, white-fire creature,
Light me with your little candle,
Ere upon my bed I lay me,
Ere in sleep I close my eyelids!"

Saw the moon rise from the water,
Rippling, rounding from the water,
Saw the flecks and shadows on it,
Whispered, "What is that, Nokomis?"
And the good Nokomis answered:
"Once a warrior, very angry,

Seized his grandmother, and threw her
Up into the sky at midnight;
Right against the moon he threw her;
'Tis her body that you see there."

Saw the rainbow in the heaven,
In the eastern sky, the rainbow,
Whispered, "What is that, Nokomis?"
And the good Nokomis answered:
" 'Tis the heaven of flowers you see there;
All the wild flowers of the forest,
All the lilies of the prairie,
When on earth they fade and perish,
Blossom in that heaven above us."

When he heard the owls at midnight,
Hooting, laughing in the forest,
"What is that?" he cried in terror;
"What is that?" he said, "Nokomis?"
And the good Nokomis answered:
"That is but the owl and owlet,
Talking in their native language,
Talking, scolding at each other."

Then the little Hiawatha
Learned of every bird its language,
Learned their names and all their secrets,

How they built their nests in Summer,
Where they hid themselves in Winter,
Talked with them whene'er he met them,
Called them "Hiawatha's Chickens."

Of all beasts he learned the language,
Learned their names and all their secrets,
How the beavers built their lodges,
Where the squirrels hid their acorns,
How the reindeer ran so swiftly,
Why the rabbit was so timid,
Talked with them whene'er he met them,
Called them "Hiawatha's Brothers."

WHAT IS PINK? A ROSE IS PINK

Christina Rossetti

What is pink? A rose is pink
    By the fountain's brink.
What is red? A poppy's red
    In its barley bed.
What is blue? The sky is blue
    Where the clouds float thro'.
What is white? A swan is white
    Sailing in the light.
What is yellow? A pear is yellow,
    Rich and ripe and mellow.
What is green? The grass is green,
    With small flowers between.
What is violet? Clouds are violet
    In the summer twilight,
What is orange? Why, an orange,
    Just an orange!

RAIN

Robert Louis Stevenson

The rain is raining all around,
    It falls on field and tree;
It rains on the umbrella here,
    And on the ships at sea.

DAME WIGGINS OF LEE

Dame Wiggins of Lee
Was a worthy old soul
As e'er threaded a needle
Or washed in a bowl;
She held mice and rats
In such antipathy,
That seven fine cats
Kept Dame Wiggins of Lee.

The rats and mice scared
By this fierce whiskered crew,
The poor seven cats
Soon had nothing to do;
So, as anyone idle
She ne'er loved to see,
She sent them to school,
Did Dame Wiggins of Lee.

The teacher soon wrote
That they all of them knew
How to read the word "milk"
And to spell the word "mew."
And they all washed their faces
Before they took tea;
"Were there ever such dears!"
Said Dame Wiggins of Lee.

But soon she grew tired
Of living alone;
So she sent for her cats
From school to come home.
Each rowing a wherry,
Returning you see:
The frolic made merry
Dame Wiggins of Lee.

The Dame was quite pleased
And ran out to market;
When she came back,
They were mending the carpet.
The needle each handled
As brisk as a bee;
"Well done, my good cats,"
Said Dame Wiggins of Lee.

To give them a treat,
She ran out for some rice.
When she came back,
They were skating on ice.
"I shall soon see one down,
Aye, perhaps two or three,
I'll bet half a crown,"
Said Dame Wiggins of Lee.

When springtime came back,
They had breakfast of curds,
And were greatly afraid
Of disturbing the birds.
"If you sit, like good cats,
All the seven in a tree,
They will teach you to sing!"
Said Dame Wiggins of Lee.

So they sat in a tree,
And said, "Beautiful! Hark!"
And they listened and looked
In the clouds for the lark.
They sang, by the fireside,
Symphoniously
A song without words
To Dame Wiggins of Lee.

They called, the next day,
On the tomtit and sparrow,
And wheeled a poor sick lamb
Home in a barrow.
"You shall all have some sprats
For your humanity,
My seven good cats,"
Said Dame Wiggins of Lee.

While she ran to the field,
To look for its dam,
They were warming the bed
For the poor sick lamb;
They turned up the clothes
All as neat as could be.
"I shall ne'er want a nurse,"
Said Dame Wiggins of Lee.

She wished them good night
And went up to bed,
When, lo! in the morning,
The cats were all fled.
But soon—what a fuss!
"Where can they all be?
Here, pussy, puss, puss!"
Cried Dame Wiggins of Lee.

The Dame's heart was nigh broke,
So she sat down to weep,
When she saw them come back
Each riding a sheep.
She fondled and patted
Each purring tommy.
"Ah, welcome, my dears!"
Said Dame Wiggins of Lee.

The Dame was unable
Her pleasure to smother
To see the sick lamb
Jump up to its mother.
In spite of the gout
And a pain in the knee,
She went dancing about,
Did Dame Wiggins of Lee.

The farmer soon heard
Where his sheep went astray,
And arrived at Dame's door
With his faithful dog, Tray.
He knocked with his crook,
And the stranger to see,
Out the window did look
Dame Wiggins of Lee.

For their kindness he had them
All drawn by his team,
And gave them some field mice
And raspberry cream.
Said he, "All my stock
You shall presently see,
For I honor the cats
Of Dame Wiggins of Lee."

He sent his maid out
For some muffins and crumpets,
And when he turned round,
They were blowing of trumpets.
Said he, "I suppose
She's as deaf as can be,
Or this ne'er could be borne
By Dame Wiggins of Lee."

To show them his poultry,
He turned them all loose,
When each nimbly leaped
On the back of a goose,
Which frightened them so
That they ran to the sea,
And half-drowned the poor cats
Of Dame Wiggins of Lee.

For the care of his lamb
And their comical pranks
He gave them a ham
And abundance of thanks.
"I wish you good day,
My fine fellows," said he.
"My compliments, pray,
To Dame Wiggins of Lee."

You see them arrived
At their Dame's welcome door.
They showed her their presents
And all their good store.
"Now, come in to supper
And sit down with me,
All welcome once more,"
Cried Dame Wiggins of Lee.

MR. NOBODY

I know a funny little man,
    As quiet as a mouse,
Who does the mischief that is done
    In everybody's house!
There's no one ever sees his face,
    And yet we all agree
That every plate we break was cracked
    By Mr. Nobody.

'Tis he who always tears our books,
    Who leaves the door ajar,
He pulls the buttons from our shirts,
    And scatters pins afar;
That squeaking door will always squeak,
    For, prithee, don't you see,
We leave the oiling to be done
    By Mr. Nobody.

The fingermarks upon the door
    By none of us are made;
We never leave the blinds unclosed,
    To let the curtains fade.
The ink we never spill; the boots
    That lying round you see
Are not our boots—they all belong
    To Mr. Nobody.

LITTLE JACK PUMPKIN FACE

Little Jack Pumpkin Face
Lived on a vine;
Little Jack Pumpkin Face
Thought it was fine.

First he was small and green,
Then big and yellow;
Little Jack Pumpkin Face
Is a fine fellow.

THE NAUGHTY BOY

John Keats

There was a naughty boy,
And a naughty boy was he,
He ran away to Scotland
The people for to see—
Then he found
That the ground
Was as hard,
That a yard
Was as long,
That a song
Was as merry,
That a cherry
Was as red,

That lead
Was as weighty,
That fourscore
Was as eighty,
That a door
Was as wooden
As in England—
So he stood in his shoes
And he wondered,
He wondered.
He stood in his shoes
And he wondered.

THE DUCK AND THE KANGAROO

Edward Lear

Said the Duck to the Kangaroo,
   "Good gracious! How you hop
Over the fields, and the water too,
   As if you never would stop!
My life is a bore in this nasty pond;
And I long to go out in the world beyond:
   I wish I could hop like you,"
   Said the Duck to the Kangaroo.

"Please give me a ride on your back,"
   Said the Duck to the Kangaroo:
"I would sit quite still, and say nothing but
     'Quack'
   The whole of the long day through;
And we'd go the Dee, and the Jelly Bo Lee,
Over the land, and over the sea:
   Please take me a ride! Oh, do!"
   Said the Duck to the Kangaroo.

Said the Kangaroo to the Duck,
   "This requires some little reflection.
Perhaps, on the whole, it might bring me
     luck:
   And there seems but one objection;

Which is, if you'll let me speak so bold,
Your feet are unpleasantly wet and cold,
   And would probably give me the roo—
   Matiz," said the Kangaroo.

Said the Duck, "As I sate on the rocks,
   I have thought over that completely;
And I bought four pairs of worsted socks,
   Which fit my web-feet neatly;
And to keep out the cold, I've bought a
      cloak;
And every day a cigar I'll smoke;
   All to follow my own dear true
   Love of a Kangaroo."

Said the Kangaroo, "I'm ready,
   All in the moonlight pale;
But to balance me well, dear Duck, sit
      steady,
   And quite at the end of my tail."
So away they went with a hop and a bound;
And they hopped the whole world three
      times round.
   And who so happy, oh! who,
   As the Duck and the Kangaroo?

CASABIANCA

Felicia Dorothea Hemans

The boy stood on the burning deck,
    Whence all but him had fled;
The flame that lit the battle's wreck
    Shone round him o'er the dead.

Yet beautiful and bright he stood,
    As born to rule the storm;
A creature of heroic blood,
    A proud though childlike form.

The flames rolled on—he would not go
    Without his father's word;
That father, faint in death below,
    His voice no longer heard.

He called aloud, "Say, Father, say
    If yet my task be done!"
He knew not that the chieftain lay
    Unconscious of his son.

"Speak, Father!" once again he cried,
    "If I may yet be gone!"
And but the booming shots replied,
    And fast the flames rolled on.

Upon his brow he felt their breath,
    And in his waving hair,
And looked from that lone post of death
    In still, yet brave despair;

And shouted but once more aloud,
    "My father! Must I stay?"
While o'er him fast, through sail and shroud,
    The wreathing fires made way.

They wrapt the ship in splendor wild,
    They caught the flag on high,
And streamed above the gallant child
    Like banners in the sky.

There came a burst of thunder sound—
    The boy—oh! where was he?
Ask of the winds that far around
    With fragments strewed the sea,

With mast, and helm, and pennon fair,
    That well had borne their part;
But the noblest thing that perished there
    Was that young faithful heart.

PICCOLA

Celia Thaxter

Poor, sweet Piccola! Did you hear
What happened to Piccola, children dear?
'Tis seldom Fortune such favor grants
As fell to this little maid of France.

'Twas Christmastime, and her parents poor
Could hardly drive the wolf from the door,
Striving with poverty's patient pain
Only to live till summer again.

No gifts for Piccola! Sad were they
When dawned the morning of Christmas
　　Day;
Their little darling no joy might stir,
St. Nicholas nothing would bring to her!

But Piccola never doubted at all
That something beautiful must befall
Every child upon Christmas Day,
And so she slept till the dawn was gray.

And full of faith, when at last she woke,
She stole to her shoe as the morning broke:
Such sounds of gladness filled all the air,
'Twas plain St. Nicholas *had* been there!

In rushed Piccola sweet, half-wild:
Never was seen such a joyful child.
"See what the good saint brought!" she
    cried,
And Mother and Father must peep inside.

Now such a story who ever heard?
There was a little shivering bird!
A sparrow, that in at the window flew,
Had crept into Piccola's tiny shoe!

"How good poor Piccola must have been!"
She cried, as happy as any queen,
While the starving sparrow she fed and
    warmed,
And danced with rapture, she was so
    charmed.

Children, this story I tell to you,
Of Piccola sweet and her bird, is true.
In the far-off land of France, they say,
Still do they live to this very day.

THREE THINGS TO REMEMBER
William Blake

A Robin Redbreast in a cage
Puts all Heaven in a rage.

A skylark wounded on the wing
Doth make a cherub cease to sing.

He who shall hurt the little wren
Shall never be beloved by men.

THE VULTURE
Hilaire Belloc

The Vulture eats between his meals,
    And that's the reason why
He very, very rarely feels
    As well as you or I.
His eye is dull, his head is bald,
    His neck is growing thinner.
Oh, what a lesson for us all
    To only eat at dinner.

EARLY TO BED

Early to bed, and early to rise,
Makes a man healthy, wealthy, and wise.

THE FRIENDLY COW

Robert Louis Stevenson

The friendly cow, all red and white,
  I love with all my heart;
She gives me cream, with all her might,
  To eat with apple-tart.

She wanders lowing here and there,
  And yet she cannot stray,
All in the pleasant open air,
  The pleasant light of day.

And blown by all the winds that pass
  And wet with all the showers,
She walks among the meadow grass
  And eats the meadow flowers.

WHEN THE COWS COME HOME

Christina Rossetti

When the cows come home, the milk is
    coming,
Honey's made while the bees are humming;
Duck and drake on the rushy lake,
And the deer live safe in the breezy brake;
And timid, funny, pert little bunny
Winks his nose, and sits all sunny.

CARPENTERS

Saw, saw, saw away,
Saw the boards and saw the timbers.
Saw, saw, saw away,
We will build a house today.

PUSSY CAT, PUSSY CAT

"Pussy Cat, Pussy Cat,
Where have you been?"
"I've been to London
To look at the Queen."

"Pussy Cat, Pussy Cat,
What did you there?"
"I frightened a little mouse
Under the chair."

THE PURPLE COW
Gelett Burgess

I never saw a purple cow,
I never hope to see one;
But this I will say, anyhow,
I'd rather see than be one.

THE MELANCHOLY PIG
Lewis Carroll

There was a Pig that sat alone,
    Beside a ruined Pump.
By day and night he made his moan:
    It would have stirred a heart of stone
To see him wring his hoofs and groan
    Because he could not jump.

THE LION
Hilaire Belloc

The Lion, the Lion, he dwells in the waste,
He has a big head and a very small waist;
But his shoulders are stark, and his jaws they
    are grim,
And a good little child will not play with him.

GOOD TIDINGS

A sunshiny shower
Won't last half an hour.

Rain before seven,
Fine by eleven.

March winds and April showers
Bring forth May flowers.

THE VIOLET

William Wordsworth

A violet by a mossy stone,
Half hidden from the eye,
Fair as a star, when only one
Is shining in the sky.

THE ICHTHYOSAURUS

There once was an Ichthyosaurus
Who lived when the earth was all porous,
But he fainted with shame
When he first heard his name,
And departed a long time before us.

CATERPILLAR

Christina Rossetti

Brown and furry
Caterpillar in a hurry
Take your walk
To the shady leaf, or stalk,
Or what not,
Which may be the chosen spot.
No toad spy you,
Hovering bird of prey pass by you;
Spin and die,
To live again a butterfly.

THE ANIMAL FAIR

I went to the animal fair.
The birds and the beasts were there.
The big baboon,
By the light of the moon,
Was combing his auburn hair.
The monkey he got drunk—
He fell on the elephant's trunk.
The elephant sneezed,
And fell on his knees,
And that was the end of the monk, the monk,
  the monk . . .

THE YOUNG LADY OF NIGER

There was a young lady of Niger
Who smiled as she rode on a tiger;
    They returned from the ride
    With the lady inside,
And the smile on the face of the tiger.

THE CLOCK

Tick, tock, tick, tock,
Merrily sings the clock;
It's time for work,
It's time for play,
So it sings throughout the day.
Tick, tock, tick, tock,
Merrily sings the clock.

I HAD A LITTLE DOGGY

I had a little Doggy that used to sit and beg;
But Doggy tumbled down the stairs and
broke his little leg.
Oh, Doggy, I will nurse you, and try to make
you well.
And you shall have a collar with a little silver
bell.
Ah, Doggy, don't you think that you should
very faithful be,
For having such a loving friend to comfort
you as me?
And when your leg is better, and you can run
and play,
We'll have a scamper in the fields and see
them making hay.

But, Doggy, you must promise (and mind
    your word you keep)
Not once to tease the little lambs, or run
    among the sheep;
And then the little yellow chicks that play
    upon the grass,
You must not even wag your tail to scare
    them as you pass.

A GAME OF TAG

A grasshopper once had a game of tag
    With some crickets that lived nearby,
When he stubbed his toe, and over he went,
    Too quick to see with your eye.

Then the crickets leaned up against a fence,
    And chirped till their sides were sore,
But the grasshopper said, "You are laughing
      at me,
    And I won't play any more."

So off he went, though he wanted to stay,
    For he was not hurt by the fall,
And the gay little crickets went on with the
      game,
    And never missed him at all.

WILD BEASTS

Evaleen Stein

I will be a lion
    And you shall be a bear,
And each of us will have a den
    Beneath a nursery chair;
And you must growl and growl and growl,
    And I will roar and roar,
And then—why, then—you'll growl again,
    And I will roar some more!

GOOD MORNING,
MERRY SUNSHINE

Good morning, merry sunshine,
How did you wake so soon?
You've scared the little stars away,
And shined away the moon;
I saw you go to sleep last night,
Before I ceased my playing.
How did you get 'way over here,
And where have you been staying?

I never go to sleep, dear;
I just go round to see
My little children of the East
Who rise and watch for me.
I waken all the birds and bees,
And flowers on the way,
And last of all the little child
Who stayed out late to play.

JOHN AND JANE

As John and Jane walked down the lane,
One very pleasant Sunday,
Said John to Jane, "Unless it rain,
Tomorrow will be Monday."

LET'S BE MERRY

Christina Rossetti

Mother shake the cherry tree,
    Susan catch a cherry;
Oh, how funny that will be,
    Let's be merry!

One for brother, one for sister,
    Two for Mother more,
Six for Father, hot and tired,
    Knocking at the door.

THE SPIDER AND THE FLY

Mary Howitt

"Will you walk into my parlor?" said the
　　spider to the fly;
" 'Tis the prettiest little parlor that ever you
　　did spy.
The way into my parlor is up a winding stair
And I have many curious things to show
　　when you are there."
"Oh, no, no," said the little fly. "To ask me is
　　in vain,
For who goes up your winding stair can ne'er
　　come down again."

"I'm sure you must be weary, dear, with soar-
　　ing up so high;
Will you rest upon my little bed?" said the
　　spider to the fly.
"There are pretty curtains drawn around;
　　the sheets are fine and thin,
And if you like to rest a while, I'll snugly tuck
　　you in!"
"Oh, no, no," said the little fly, "for I've often
　　heard it said,

They never, never wake again who sleep
   upon your bed!"

Said the cunning spider to the fly: "Dear
   friend, what can I do
To prove the warm affection I've always felt
   for you?
I have within my pantry good store of all
   that's nice;
I'm sure you're very welcome—will you
   please to take a slice?"
"Oh, no, no," said the little fly. "Kind sir, that
   cannot be.
I've heard what's in your pantry, and I do
   not wish to see!"

"Sweet creature," said the spider, "you're
   witty and you're wise;
How handsome are your gauzy wings! How
   brilliant are your eyes!
I have a little looking glass upon my parlor
   shelf;
If you'll step in one moment, dear, you shall
   behold yourself."
"I thank you, gentle sir," she said, "for what
   you're pleased to say,
And, bidding you good morning now, I'll call
   another day."

The spider turned him round about and went
    into his den,
For well he knew the silly fly would soon
    come back again.

So he wove a subtle web in a little corner sly,
And set his table ready to dine upon the fly;
Then came out to his door again, and merrily
    did sing:
"Come hither, hither, pretty fly, with the
    pearl and silver wing;
Your robes are green and purple; there's a
    crest upon your head;
Your eyes are like the diamond bright, but
    mine are dull as lead!"

Alas, alas! How very soon this silly little fly,
Hearing his wily, flattering words, came
    slowly flitting by;
With buzzing wings she hung aloft, then
    near and nearer drew,
Thinking only of her brilliant eyes and green
    and purple hue,
Thinking only of her crested head. Poor,
    foolish thing! At last,
Up jumped the cunning spider, and fiercely
    held her fast;

He dragged her up his winding stair, into his
  dismal den.
Within his little parlor—but she ne'er came
  out again!

And now, dear little children, who may this
  story read,
To idle, silly, flattering words I pray you
  ne'er give heed;
Unto an evil counselor close heart and ear
  and eye,
And take a lesson from this tale of the spider
  and the fly.

BE LIKE THE BIRD
Victor Hugo

Be like the bird, who
Halting in his flight
On limb too slight
Feels it give way beneath him,
Yet sings,
Knowing he hath wings.

THE POSTMAN

The whistling postman swings along.
   His bag is deep and wide,
And messages from all the world
   Are bundled up inside.

The postman's walking up our street,
   Soon now he'll ring my bell.
Perhaps there'll be a letter stamped
   In Asia. Who can tell?

Use this easy, convenient way to build your child's library of
Read-Aloud Books